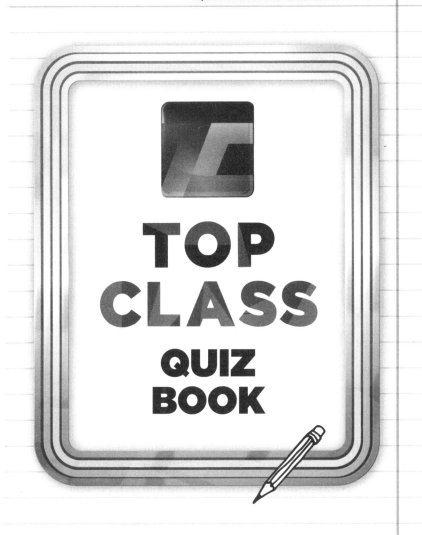

TOP
CLASS
QUIZ
BOOK

TOP
CLASS
QUIZ
BOOK

ORCHARD

ORCHARD BOOKS
First published in Great Britain in 2019 by
The Watts Publishing Group

1 3 5 7 9 10 8 6 4 2

A CIP catalogue record for this book
is available from the British Library.

ISBN 978 1 40835 9907

Printed and bound in Great Britain by
Clays Ltd, Elcograf S.p.A.

The paper and board used in this book are made
from wood from responsible sources

Black and white illustrations © Shutterstock: VectorPixelStar;
Tom and Kwikki; strogaya; Tiwat K; kay mosk; Nikolaeva
19 top left MyStocks; top right Sunset And Sea Design;
bottom left Cat_arch_angel; bottom right Lecka

Orchard Books
An imprint of Hachette Children's Group
Part of The Watts Publishing Group Limited
Carmelite House, 50 Victoria Embankment,
London EC4Y 0DZ

An Hachette UK Company
www.hachette.co.uk
www.hachettechildrens.co.uk

CONTENTS

7 WELCOME TO TOP CLASS!

9 ENGLISH

33 MATHS

63 SCIENCE

93

HISTORY

121

GEOGRAPHY

TEST THE TEACHER

161

179

ANSWERS

WELCOME TO
TOP CLASS!

Top Class is CBBC's hit quiz show. Each series tests children and their teachers in the search for the UK's smartest school.

Using questions from previous series, and some brand new ones too, test yourself to see if you could beat the best.

Covering topics including English, Maths, Science, Geography and History, you'll be able to find out what are your weakest or strongest subjects. Or maybe you're already Top of the Class!

At the end of the book are some questions that you can ask your teachers. Will they be up for the challenge or tested by the task? Can you answer them yourself? You could even ask your friends and family if they can answer any of the questions.

If you get stuck at any point, all of the answers are at the back of the book, but – no peeking until you're completely out of ideas! You can always move on and come back to questions later. You don't have to go through the book in order. Take your pick and start with your favourite subject first.

Whether you enjoy multiple choice or missing words quizzes, crosswords, word jumbles or word searches, there are many different types of questions to keep you entertained for hours!

Now, find out if you have what it takes to be Top Class!

ENGLISH

ENGLISH: Opposites

1. Which word means the opposite
of the word 'exterior'?

> a) interior   b) extinct   c) interim

2. Which word means the opposite
of the word 'guilty'?

> a) innocent
> b) innocuous
> c) legitimate

3. Which word is the opposite
of the word 'junior'?

> a) minor   b) senior   c) inferior

4. Which word means the opposite of the word 'vertical', as in the sentence 'The flag of France has three vertical stripes'?

a) angled
b) horizontal
c) aligned

5. Which word means the opposite of the word 'minimum', as in the sentence 'Josh did the minimum amount of homework required'?

a) ultimate   b) total   c) maximum

6. Which word means the opposite of the word 'public', as in the sentence 'The videos on my vlog channel are public'?

a) private   b) permitted   c) proper

1. In poetry, which word beginning with 'P' means describing animals and objects as having human qualities?

a) personification

b) personalised

c) people

2. In poetry, what 'A' is the name of a technique where words that start with the same sound are placed close together?

a) aligned

b) arranged

c) alliteration

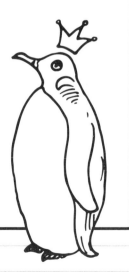

3. In poetry, what 'S' is a figure of speech where one thing is compared to another, as in the phrase 'as tall as a mountain'?

a) similar

b) simile

c) same

4. Which word beginning with 'M' can mean both a unit of length, and the rhythm of a poem?

a) mile

b) metre

c) millimetre

5. Haiku, ballad and limerick are all specific types of which form of writing?

a) report

b) poem

c) non-fiction

ENGLISH: Punctuation

1. What is the name of the punctuation mark that consists of three dots in a row?

a) ellipsis
b) pause
c) break

2. Which punctuation mark has a shape like a hook over a full stop?

a) question mark
b) exclamation mark
c) rude mark

3. What is the name of the round dot at the end of sentences?

a) end mark
b) full stop
c) end stop

4. Which sentence correctly uses an apostrophe?

a) The mans 'hat blew off in the strong wind.
b) The mans' hat blew off in the strong wind.
c) The man's hat blew off in the strong wind.

5. Which sentence is correctly capitalised?

a) Fred and george had to get to Saint edward's school by eight o'clock.

b) Fred and George had to get to saint Edward's school by eight o'clock.

c) Fred and George had to get to Saint Edward's school by eight o'clock.

6. What is another name for an inverted comma?

a) a full stop

b) a quote mark

c) an apostrophe

7. Which punctuation mark has a comma with a full stop on top of it?

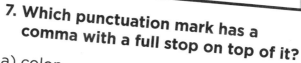

a) colon

b) semicolon

c) ellipsis

8. What does a conjunction do?

a) It links two words or phrases together.

b) It describes words.

c) It refers to a future time.

☑ True or false? ✗

1. **The superlative form of the word 'much' is 'most'.**

   ☑ ☐   ☐ ✗

2. **The superlative form of the word 'good' is 'bad'.**

   ☑ ☐   ☐ ✗

3. **In the phrase 'Chestnuts roasting on an open fire', the word 'on' is a preposition.**

   ☑ ☐   ☐ ✗

4. **Proper nouns name specific people, places or things, such as 'Glasgow' or 'Susan'.**

   ☑ ☐   ☐ ✗

5. **In the words 'tricycle' and 'triangle', the prefix 'tri' indicates the number four.**

   ☑ ☐   ☐ ✗

6. In the words 'centimetre' and 'century', the prefix 'cent' indicates the number 100.

☑ ☐   ☐ ☒

7. In the words 'autograph' and 'calligraphy', the suffix 'graph' refers to writing.

☑ ☐   ☐ ☒

8. In the sentence 'The small man spoke quickly', the word 'spoke' is a noun.

☑ ☐   ☐ ☒

9. In the sentence 'The parcel was heavy but he managed to deliver it', the word 'managed' is a conjunction.

☑ ☐   ☐ ☒

10. In the sentence 'The concert tickets were under Steve's wallet', the word 'under' is a preposition.

☑ ☐   ☐ ☒

Circle the correct words.

1. courageous   couragous   courajous

2. rithym   rithum   rhythm

3. soleum   solemn   solum

4. receive   recieve   recive

5. accommodate   acommodate   accomodate

6. embarrass   enbarrass   enbarass

Complete the correct spelling of the names of the flowers in the pictures.

D _ _ _ Y

D _ F _ _ _ _ L

T H _ S _ _ _

V _ _ _ _ T

ENGLISH: Missing words

> ## Write the correct word into these sentences.

1. The frog _____ over the lily pad.

> jumped
> jumping
> jumper

2.

> quicker
> quickly
> quick

The leopard was _____ than the rabbit.

3. The bees were _____ around the flowers looking for nectar.

buzzing   buzzed   buzzer

4. Ellie _____ the ball and so Jack was out of the game.

caught   catched   cooked

5. Can you see what's happening over _____?

their
they're
there

6. If he ate a _____ Brussels sprout, then he was going to get ice cream for dessert.

hole   whole   mole

7. At Christmas, I _____ 50 Christmas cards.

scent   sent   cent

ENGLISH: Word search

P	T	E	N	S	E	N	S
R	P	X	A	H	O	S	U
A	R	E	N	O	U	N	F
D	E	X	E	M	I	F	F
V	F	F	W	O	R	D	I
E	I	L	T	N	O	R	X
R	X	S	R	Y	E	O	L
B	O	N	M	M	R	N	E

NOUN
ADVERB
WORD
TENSE
PREFIX
SUFFIX
HOMONYM

ENGLISH: Word formation

1. Which five-letter word can be placed after GREEN, LIGHT and WARE to make three new words?

GREEN _ _ _ _ _
LIGHT _ _ _ _ _
WARE _ _ _ _ _

2. Which five-letter word can be placed before MARKET, MAN and STAR to make three new words?

_ _ _ _ _ MARKET
_ _ _ _ _ MAN
_ _ _ _ _ STAR

3. Which five-letter word can be placed after SURF, CUP, SIDE, BLACK and SKATE to make five new words?

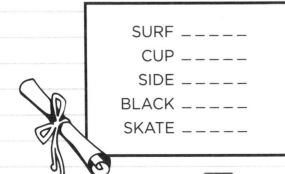

SURF _ _ _ _ _
CUP _ _ _ _ _
SIDE _ _ _ _ _
BLACK _ _ _ _ _
SKATE _ _ _ _ _

ENGLISH: Homophones

Which of the two homophones given correctly completes each of the following sentences?

1. The dog is wagging its **tail / tale**.

2. Sarah was **board / bored** of playing videogames.

3. Louise could not decide what to **wear / where** to the party.

4. Steven had to **alter / altar** his plans due to the weather.

5. Selena could not decide **weather / whether** to go to the concert with her friends.

6. Owen Farrell **threw / through** the rugby ball to Chris Robshaw.

7. There are seven days in the **week / weak**.

8. Adam Peaty had a bowl of **cereal / serial** before training.

ENGLISH: Grammar crossword

CLUES:

Down

1. Noun: a clear liquid.

2. Adverb: this describes how a snail moves

3. Proper noun: a famous boxer, Muhammad _____ .

5. Article.

6. Preposition: the opposite of 'under'.

Across

4. Adjective: something that is red, green, blue, yellow and purple is very _____ .

5. Verb (infinitive): when you eat, you chew your food first, then you need _____ it.

ENGLISH: More spelling

 **Circle the correct words.**

1. preferred   preffered   prefferred

2. poisonnous   poisonous   poysonous

3. neighbour   neighbor   nayber

4. predjudice   prejudice   predyudice

5. communicate   comunicate   comunnicate

6. cemetery   cemetry   semetery

7. fourty   forty   fortie

8. awkward   aukward   auckward

9. disastrus   dissastros   disastrous

10. symbol   simbo   symble

11. comittee   commitee   committee

12. consious   conshush   conscious

13. agressive   aggresive   aggressive

14. dictionary   dictionery   dictionarie

15. exagerate   exaggerate   exsaggerate

16. sincerely   sinserely   sinseerly

ENGLISH: More missing words

> ## Write the correct word into these sentences.

1. Pens, paper, pencils, sharpeners – Lily loved all types of _____.

stationery	stationary

2. After getting up at 6 am this morning, going to sports day and then swimming club after school, Michael was now feeling very _____.

weary	wary

3. It was early in the _____ and the sun had just risen.

morning	mourning

4. In the distance, I could see the shepherd leading his _____ of sheep over the hill.

| herd | heard |

5. "Can I give you a piece of _____?" said Kendrie's grandfather.

| advise | advice |

6. I need to _____ now so that I'm the best in basketball _____ tomorrow afternoon.

| practise | practice |

7. The bride walked down the _____ of the church.

| aisle | isle |

ENGLISH: Word jumbles

1. What name is given to a word or phrase that is spelled the same backwards as forwards?

M A P L I E N D R O

_ _ _ _ _ _ _ _ _

2. When referring to books, which word beginning with 'N' means the person or character who is telling the story?

R A N R A R O T

_ _ _ _ _ _ _ _

3. What word beginning with 'O' means a word that sounds like its meaning, such as 'crunch' or 'hoot'?

T O P E I O A N O O M A

_ _ _ _ _ _ _ _ _ _ _

4. What word means the writer of a book, newspaper article or journal?

R O U T A H

_ _ _ _ _ _

5. In which book could you find out words that have the same or similar meanings?

S E A S U R U T H

_ _ _ _ _ _ _ _ _

6. What word means made up, invented or imagined?

I N C O F I T

_ _ _ _ _ _ _

7. Where can you find out about the meaning of words?

A R O Y C T I N I D

_ _ _ _ _ _ _ _ _ _

8. What word means a phrase that describes something by comparing it to some other thing?

R E P A T H O M

_ _ _ _ _ _ _ _

ENGLISH: Word search

A	S	T	B	R	F	L	Z
S	P	E	L	L	I	N	G
E	T	R	M	S	C	X	R
P	A	O	N	T	T	N	A
S	T	A	R	Y	I	A	M
L	U	P	I	Y	O	R	M
R	E	A	D	I	N	G	A
U	F	G	M	E	O	P	R

POEM
GRAMMAR
SPELLING
FICTION
STORY
READING

MATHS

MATHS: Shapes

1. **How many faces does a cube have?**

> a) four   b) six   c) eight

2. **Which word beginning with 'Q' means a two-dimensional shape that has four sides?**

> a) quadrilateral
> b) quadruplet
> c) quadricep

3. **Which word beginning with 'C' means a straight-sided tube with circular ends?**

> a) circloid   b) cycloid   c) cylinder

4. **Which word beginning with 'E' is used to describe any polygon whose sides are all the same length?**

> a) equable
> b) equilateral
> c) equalised

5. If a circle has a radius of 6 centimetres, what is the length of its diameter?

a) 6 centimetres

b) 12 centimetres

c) 24 centimetres

6. If you multiply the number of sides on a pentagon by the number of sides on an octagon, what number do you get?

a) 40   b) 45   c) 58

7. If you multiply the number of sides on a hexagon by the number of sides on a trapezium, what number do you get?

a) 18   b) 24   c) 30

8. How many faces does a tetrahedron have?

a) 4   b) 6   c) 10

MATHS: True or false?

1. A cube has four corners.

☑ ☐   ☐ ☒

2. The area of a rectangle that is 12 centimetres long, and 6 centimetres wide. is 72 centimetre squared.

☑ ☐   ☐ ☒

3. A parallelogram has four sides.

☑ ☐   ☐ ☒

4. A rhombus has eight sides.

☑ ☐   ☐ ☒

5. A decagon has four sides.

☑ ☐   ☐ ☒

6. Geometry comes from Greek words meaning 'Earth measurement' and means the mathematical study of shapes.

☑ ☐   ☐ ☒

MATHS: Shapes word search

B	G	C	E	N	O	C	H
T	R	I	A	N	G	L	E
E	M	R	L	H	Q	B	X
O	S	C	Y	B	U	R	A
V	Z	L	F	C	J	N	G
A	P	E	I	X	Y	K	O
L	S	Q	U	A	R	E	N
S	U	B	M	O	H	R	A

CONE
TRIANGLE
CUBE
SQUARE
RHOMBUS
HEXAGON
OVAL
CIRCLE

1. How many degrees are there in a right angle?

a) 45 degrees
b) 90 degrees
c) 180 degrees

2. Which word beginning with 'A' is used to describe an angle smaller than 90 degrees?

a) acute
b) accent
c) adjacent

3. Which word beginning with 'P' means a tool used to measure the size of angles?

a) protractor
b) prototype
c) prism

4. If I am facing north-east and I turn clockwise 90 degrees, which direction am I now facing?

a) south-west

b) south

c) south-east

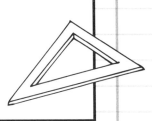

5. If two angles in a triangle add up to 130 degrees, what is the size of the third angle?

a) 50 degrees

b) 90 degrees

c) 130 degrees

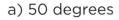

6. In maths, which word beginning with 'P' describes two lines that meet at a right angle?

a) protracted

b) parallel

c) perpendicular

1. A baker's dozen is a group or set of how many things?

a) 12
b) 13
c) 24

2. How many millimetres are there in 10 centimetres?

a) 100
b) 1,000
c) 10,000

3. How many centimetres are there in five metres?

a) 50
b) 500
c) 5,000

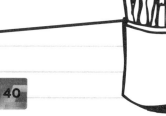

4. If one teaspoon holds 5 millilitres of water, then how many teaspoons of water make up one litre?

a) 20
b) 100
c) 200

5. How many grams are there in a quarter of a kilogram?

a) 25
b) 250
c) 500

6. How many grams are there in a kilogram?

a) 100
b) 1,000
c) 10,000

7. How many years are there in a millennium?

a) 100
b) 500
c) 1,000

MATHS: Fractions

1. Which word beginning with 'N' is the name given to the number above the line in a fraction?

| a) nonagon | b) numen | c) numerator |

2. Liam's family has 3 dogs, 4 cats and 5 hamsters. What fraction of Liam's pets are dogs? Give your answer in its simplest form.

| a) 1/4 | b) 1/3 | c) 1/2 |

3. What is the lowest common denominator of both one-quarter and one-third?

| a) 6 | b) 12 | c) 24 |

4. What is one-third multiplied by one-quarter? Give your answer as a fraction in its simplest form.

a) 1/12

b) 1/6

c) 1/3

5. Express 10% as a fraction in its simplest form.

a) 1/100   b) 1/10   c) 1/5

6. Calculate 1/2 + 1/4. Give your answer as a fraction in its simplest form.

a) 2/6   b) 3/6   c) 3/4

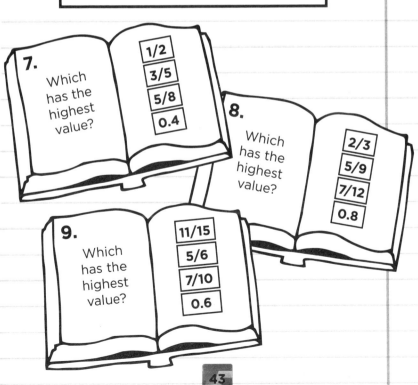

7. Which has the highest value?

1/2
3/5
5/8
0.4

8. Which has the highest value?

2/3
5/9
7/12
0.8

9. Which has the highest value?

11/15
5/6
7/10
0.6

MATHS: Numbers

1. What is 5 squared?

| 25 | 50 | 100 |

2. What is 6 squared?

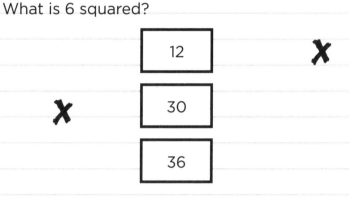

| 12 |

| 30 |

| 36 |

3. What is the square root of 81?

| 8 | 9 | 11 |

4. What is the square root of 144?

| 11 | 12 | 13 |

5. Which word beginning with 'P' means a number that can only be evenly divided by itself and one?

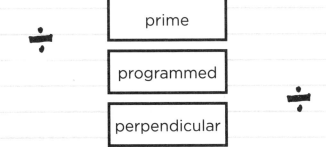

prime

programmed

perpendicular

6. What is the next square number after 49?

| 55 | 64 | 81 |

7. What is the next prime number after 11?

13

15

31

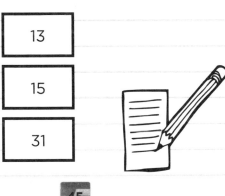

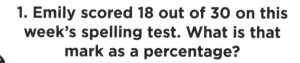

1. Emily scored 18 out of 30 on this week's spelling test. What is that mark as a percentage?

a) 50%   b) 60%   c) 80%

2. Last season, Olivia took 15 penalties. She scored from 12 of them. What percentage did she miss?

a) 3%   b) 20%   c) 35%

3. Amber has two cats and eight hamsters. Given in its lowest form, what is the ratio of cats to hamsters here?

a) 1:4   b) 1:6   c) 1:8

4. Using a normal six-sided dice, what is the probability of throwing a 1, 2 or a 3 in a single roll?

a) 1/3   b) 1/2   c) 5/6

5. If I make 10 attempts on goal, and I convert 20% of these chances, how many goals will I score?

a) 1 b) 2 c) 5

6. What is 70 multiplied by 1.5?

a) 45 b) 70 c) 105

7. Calculate the size of the angle marked 'a'.

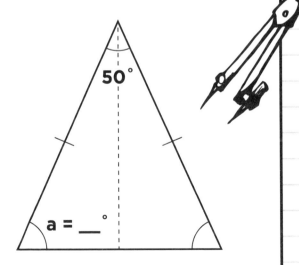

50°

a = ___°

MATHS: Sequences

1.

Find the next term in the following sequences:

a) 164, 160, 156, 152, ___

b) 3, 9, 27, 81, ___

c) 6, 6, 12, 18, 30, 48, ___

d) 108, 101, 95, 90, 86, ___

e) 38, 36, 34, 32, ___

f) 7, 14, 21, 28, ___

g) 5, 8, 12, 17, 23, ___

h) 3, 3, 6, 9, 15, 24, 39, ___

2. What is the sixth term in this sequence?

154, 143, 132, 121, ___,

3. What is the sixth term in this sequence?

2916, 972, 324, 108, ___,

4. What is the seventh term
in this sequence?

5.75, 6.5, 7.25, 8, 8.75, ___,

5. What is the sixth term in this sequence?

5, 10, 15, 20, ___,

6. What is the fifth term
in this sequence?

9, 18, 36, ___,

7. What is the eighth term
in this sequence?

387, 379, 372, 366, 361, ___, ___,

MATHS: Work it out

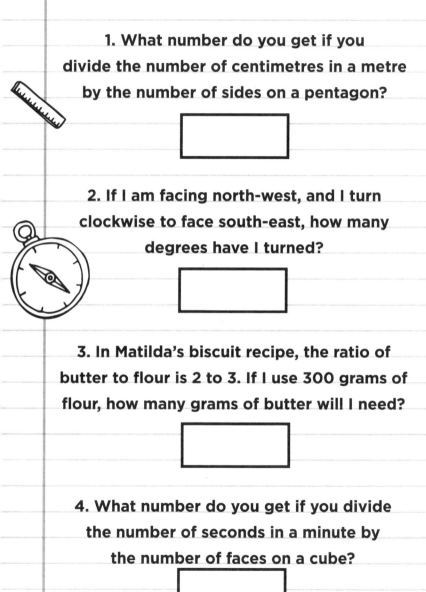

1. What number do you get if you divide the number of centimetres in a metre by the number of sides on a pentagon?

2. If I am facing north-west, and I turn clockwise to face south-east, how many degrees have I turned?

3. In Matilda's biscuit recipe, the ratio of butter to flour is 2 to 3. If I use 300 grams of flour, how many grams of butter will I need?

4. What number do you get if you divide the number of seconds in a minute by the number of faces on a cube?

5. Ellie scored 80% on last week's maths test. She answered 32 questions correctly. How many questions were on the test?

6. What decimal number is equivalent to one-quarter?

7. What is the next square number after 16?

8. What is the inverse operation of addition?

9. How many lines of symmetry does a square have?

1. Which word beginning with 'C' can mean both a combination of musical notes and a straight line joining two points on the circumference of a circle?

C _ _ _ D

2. What 'V' is a type of diagram that uses overlapping circles to represent overlapping sets of data?

V _ N _

3. Which word beginning with 'M' can refer both to something cruel or unkind, and to a type of average in statistics, calculated by adding together all the numbers in a set and dividing by the number of numbers?

M _ A _

4. Beginning with 'P', which chart representing information as slices of a circle shares its name with a type of food?

P _ _

5. Which word beginning with 'D' refers to the numbers 0 to 9, but also means a finger, thumb or toe?

D _ _ _ T

6. Which word beginning with 'N' is the name given to the number above the line in a fraction?

D _ N _ M _ _ _ _ _ R

7. In maths, what name beginning with 'C' is given to the perimeter of a circle?

C _ _ C _ _ F _ _ _ N _ _

MATHS: More shapes

1. What is the name of this specific type of triangle?

. . . .

2. What is the name of this specific type of quadrilateral?

. . . .

3. What is the name of this specific type of quadrilateral?

. . . .

4. What is the name of this specific type of quadrilateral?

. . . .

5. What is the name of this regular polygon?

. . . .

6. What is the name of this regular polygon?

. . . .

MATHS: Roman numerals

1. **In Roman numerals, what single letter is used to represent the number 1000?**

a) V   b) M   c) C

2. **In Roman numerals, the letter 'V' is used to represent which number?**

a) 10

b) 15

c) 5

3. **In Roman numerals, the letter 'C' is used to represent which number?**

a) 100   b) 50   c) 75

4. **In Roman numerals, which letter is used to represent the number ten?**

a) V

b) X

c) C

5. If a Roman soldier is XXV years old, how old would he be in our number system?

a) 3
b) 25
c) 205

6. In Roman numerals, which letter is used to represent the number 50?

a) L   b) V   c) X

7. In Roman numerals, the letter 'D' is used to represent which number?

a) 50   b) 5   c) 500

8. What number do you get if you add these Roman numerals together?
X + L + C =

a) 140   b) 160   c) 260

1. In his last tennis match, Rafael served 25 first serves. 5 of those serves went out. What percentage of his first serves were in?

. . . .

2. Ella made 95 cupcakes for the school bake sale. If she sold 80% of them, how many did she sell?

. . . .

3. There are 99 people on a train. If two-thirds of these people get off at the next station, how many people are left on the train?

. . . .

4. A standard running track is 400 metres long. How many laps of a standard track will an athlete run to complete a 10,000 metre race?

. . . .

5. Nicole wants to buy three magazines, each costing £1.30. She gives a five-pound note to the cashier. How much change should she receive?

. . . .

6. Ed Meavan gave a secret performance last night in a venue with 155 seats. 80% of the tickets were sold. How many empty seats were there?

 . . . .

7. At the school fete, Nadia sold 13 cakes, priced at 60p each. Giving your answer in pounds and pence, how much money did Nadia make from these sales?

. . . .

MATHS: Quick-fire

1. Calculate 50% of 56

2. Calculate 75% of 88

3. Calculate 20% of 110

4. Calculate 40% of 50

5. Calculate three-ninths of 72

6. Calculate 364 ÷ 7

7. Calculate 256 ÷ 8

8. Calculate 591 ÷ 3

9. Calculate 273 ÷ 3

10. Calculate 59 x 3

11. Calculate 114 x 8

12. Calculate 173 x 6

MATHS: Quick-fire

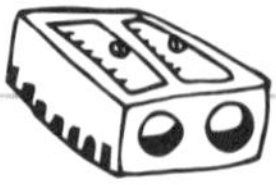

13. Calculate 72 x 6

14. Calculate 7 squared

15. Calculate 6.35 + 8.45

16. Calculate 7.25 x 6

17. Calculate 0.1 x 10

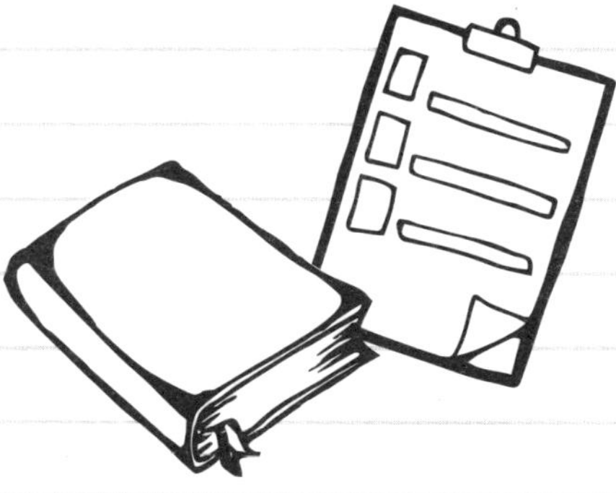

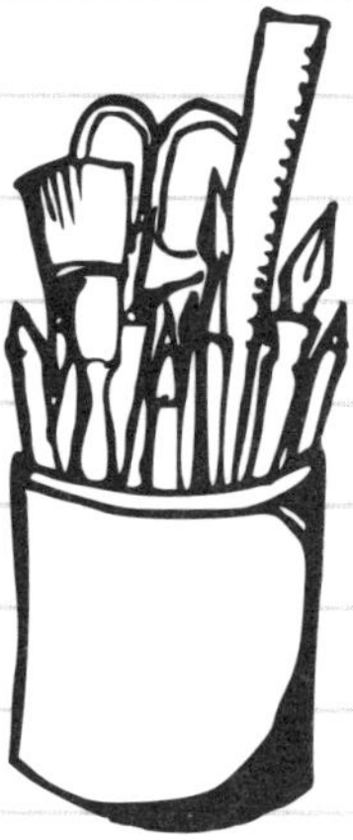

SCIENCE

SCIENCE: Human body

1. **Human blood cells can be classified as red and which other colour?**

a) blue   b) yellow   c) white

2. **The three main types of human teeth are molars, canines, and which other?**

a) cavities
b) enzymes
c) incisors

3. **What 'T' is a term for the tissue that connects muscles to bones?**

a) tendon   b) triceps   c) tibia

4. When blood passes through the lungs, it picks up oxygen and leaves behind which other gas?

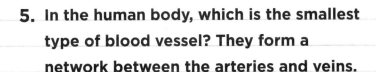

> a) carbon monoxide
>
> b) carbon dioxide
>
> c) sulphur dioxide

5. In the human body, which is the smallest type of blood vessel? They form a network between the arteries and veins.

> a) arteries   b) capillaries   c) axons

6. Which organ of the body is made up of parts including the cornea, iris and pupil?

> a) brain   b) eyes   c) liver

SCIENCE: In the mouth

CLUES:

Down

1. What type of tooth is generally the most pointed?

2. What fleshy part of the mouth lies around the roots of the teeth?

3. What type of tooth at the back of the mouth is used for grinding food?

4. The top part of a tooth shares its name with what type of headwear worn by kings and queens?

Across

5. What is the name of the hard, glossy substance that covers teeth?

6. Taste buds can be found on which muscular organ in the mouth?

SCIENCE: True or false?

1. Insects have eight legs.

☑ ☐   ☐ ☒

2. Herbivores eat both plants and meat.

☑ ☐   ☐ ☒

3. Long-nosed and Vampire are both species of bat.

☑ ☐   ☐ ☒

4. Sand, Tiger and Nurse are a species of fox.

☑ ☐   ☐ ☒

5. Ants and butterflies are both types of insect.

☑ ☐   ☐ ☒

6. Sumatran, Siberian and Bengal are all types of bear.

☑ ☐   ☐ ☒

SCIENCE: Birds word search

P	E	N	G	U	I	N	T
W	G	D	C	F	W	F	S
O	L	Y	F	R	A	N	P
O	P	A	R	R	O	T	A
K	Q	E	O	H	W	W	R
C	K	C	U	D	L	P	R
U	I	R	X	T	N	C	O
C	A	G	O	O	S	E	W

PENGUIN
CROW
PARROT
DUCK
GOOSE
SPARROW
CUCKOO
OWL

SCIENCE: Classifying animals

Find four animals that fit under each heading below, according to their body covering.

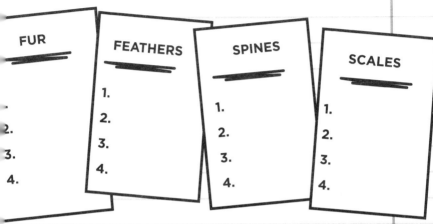

FUR

1.
2.
3.
4.

FEATHERS

1.
2.
3.
4.

SPINES

1.
2.
3.
4.

SCALES

1.
2.
3.
4.

alligator   emu   bear

        echidna   blackbird

turtle   condor   hedgehog

beaver   sea urchin   opossum

        adder   gecko

wolf   quetzal   porcupine

SCIENCE: Animals

1. **The zebra is native to which continent?**

a) South America

b) Asia

c) Africa

2. **How many legs should one ostrich, one bee and one spider normally have in total?**

a) 12   b) 16   c) 18

3. **Which breed of dog shares its name with the ship on which Charles Darwin sailed around the world?**

a) spaniel   b) beagle   c) greyhound

4. **Which word means both a type of tooth, and a family of animals that includes dogs and wolves?**

a) canine

b) mongrel

c) molar

5. The platypus, the dingo and the koala are all animals native to which country?

a) New Zealand
b) Australia
c) Madagascar

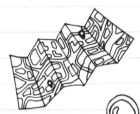

6. The Giant Panda is native to which Asian country?

a) Japan   b) China   c) India

7. Which part of a scorpion's body contains its venomous stinger?

a) pincers   b) mouth   c) tail

8. What 'E' is the name of a large, flightless bird native to Australia?

a) emu   b) elephant bird   c) eagle

1. Sugars and starches are types of which one of the five major food groups?

a) vitamins
b) carbohydrates
c) fibre

2. Fish, meat and eggs are all good sources of which type of nutrient beginning with 'P'?

a) protein
b) pathogen
c) prolactin

3. Which organ produces bile, to aid the digestion of fat?

a) kidneys
b) stomach
c) liver

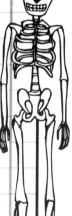

4. Red meat, spinach and broccoli are good sources of which mineral beginning with 'I', needed for producing haemoglobin in the blood?

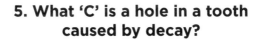

a) iodine
b) insulin
c) iron

5. What 'C' is a hole in a tooth caused by decay?

a) cavity
b) cross-section
c) cut

6. The pancreas produces which of these hormones?

a) oestrogen
b) insulin
c) testosterone

SCIENCE: The planets

☑ True or false? ☒

1. Uranus is the planet in our solar system that comes last alphabetically.

☑ ☐   ☐ ☒

2. Pluto and Ceres are types of dwarf planet.

☑ ☐   ☐ ☒

3. In our solar system, Mars is the planet with the shortest name.

☑ ☐   ☐ ☒

4. There is an asteroid belt in our solar system found between Mars and Jupiter.

☑ ☐   ☐ ☒

5. Ganymede and Io are moons of the planet Neptune.

☑ ☐   ☐ ☒

In order of their distance from the Sun,
write a list below of planets in our solar system,
starting with the closest first.

MERCURY

EARTH

JUPITER

NEPTUNE

1. The adjective 'lunar' relates to which objects in space?

a) moons
b) stars
c) asteroids

2. Which word beginning with 'T' is a scientific instrument used to look at objects in space?

a) telegraph
b) telescope
c) terrestrial

3. Which force holds planets in their orbits?

a) gravity
b) air resistance
c) friction

4. In astronomy, which word beginning with 'C' means a cluster of visible stars that appear to form a pattern when viewed from Earth, such as 'Orion' or 'Ursa Major'?

a) consolation
b) consignment
c) constellation

5. The galaxy that contains our solar system is known as the 'Milky – WHAT'?

. . . .

6. Hale-Bopp and Halley's are named examples of what type of icy astronomical object?

a) comet
b) moon
c) star

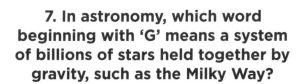

7. In astronomy, which word beginning with 'G' means a system of billions of stars held together by gravity, such as the Milky Way?

a) Galileo b) galaxy c) granit

8. In our solar system, which is the 5th planet from the Sun?

. . . .

9. In our solar system, how many planets are closer to the Sun than Earth is?

. . . .

10. What 'C' is a ball of ice and dust that moves through outer space, leaving a tail behind it?

. . . .

A	R	E	T	I	P	U	J
S	N	S	V	K	A	P	T
T	K	O	P	O	N	L	S
E	R	E	O	G	I	U	R
R	F	C	O	M	E	T	A
O	S	U	N	H	Q	O	M
I	P	B	T	J	L	N	G
D	M	G	A	L	A	X	Y

JUPITER
COMET
GALAXY
ASTEROID
MARS
SUN
MOON
PLUTO

SCIENCE: Plants

1. To make food by photosynthesis, plants need light, carbon dioxide, chlorophyll and what other substance?

a) oxygen
b) water
c) blood

2. What word beginning with 'N' is the name of a sweet liquid made by flowers that attracts insects?

a) nectar
b) nitrogen
c) nectarine

3. Hay fever is an allergic reaction to which powdery substance produced by flowering plants, beginning with the letter 'P'?

a) petals
b) pollen
c) pollution

4. Acorns are the nuts of which type of tree?

a) oak
b) chestnut
c) pine

5. What is the name given to the layer of a forest that contains the uppermost branches?

a) shrub layer
b) understory
c) canopy

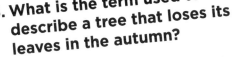

6. What is the term used to describe a tree that loses its leaves in the autumn?

a) evergreen
b) deciduous
c) shrubbery

7. Which plant has jagged leaves and is covered with stinging hairs?

a) nettle
b) rose
c) lemongrass

S _ _ _ _ _

P _ _ _ _ _

S _ _ _

R _ _ _ _

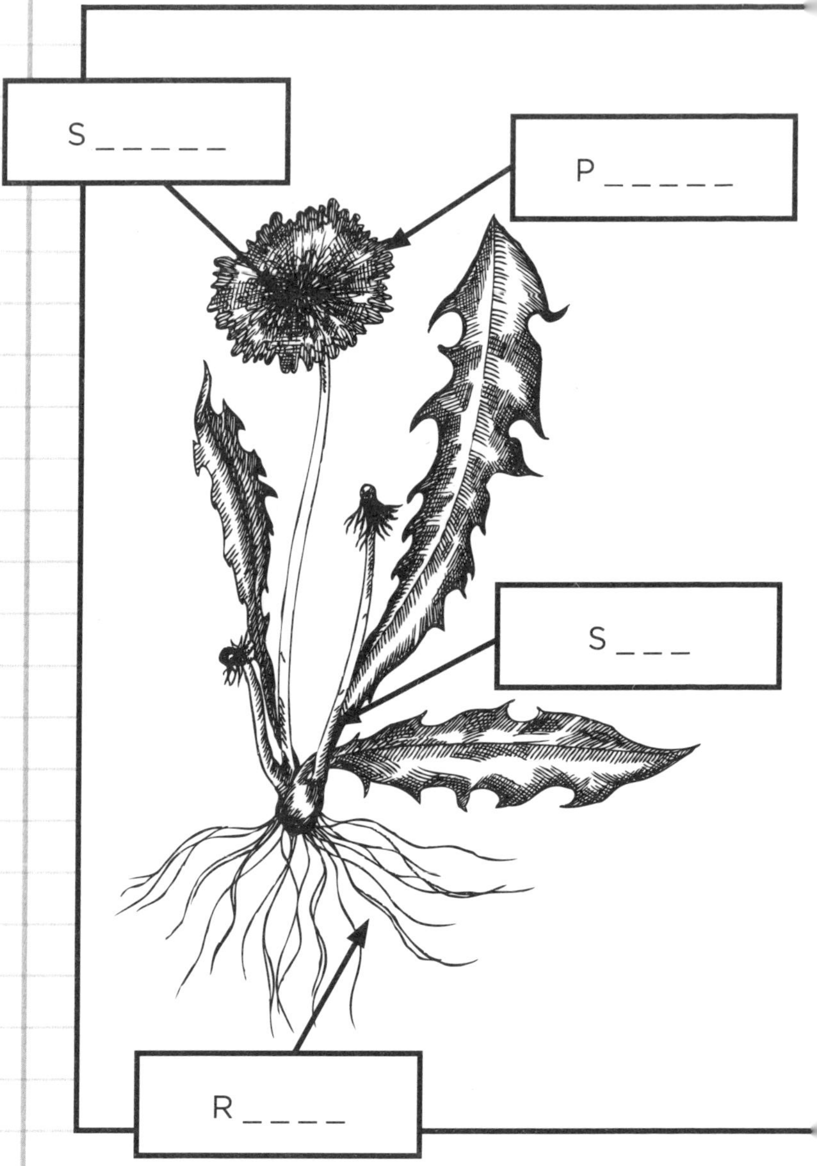

1. Which part of a plant makes pollen?

S _ _ _ _ _

2. Which part of a plant absorbs water and nutrients?

R_ _ _ _

3. Which part of a plant attracts insects?

P _ _ _ _ _

4. Which part of a plant transports nutrients to the leaves and flowers?

S _ _ _

SCIENCE: Bones

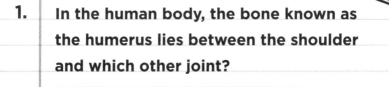

1. In the human body, the bone known as the humerus lies between the shoulder and which other joint?

a) elbow   b) wrist   c) neck

2. Which vitamin is essential for healthy bones, and is mostly obtained from sunlight?

a) vitamin A
b) vitamin D
c) vitamin E

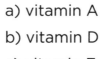

3. In the human body, the bones known as the tibia and fibula lie between the knee and which other joint?

a) ankle   b) hip   c) wrist

4. The femur is a bone in which part of the human body?

a) leg   b) arm   c) head

5. Milk and kale are good sources of which nutritional mineral beginning with 'C', which helps bones and teeth stay strong?

a) calcium
b) cholesterol
c) cells

6. How many bones does an adult human body contain?

a) around 206
b) around 306
c) around 106

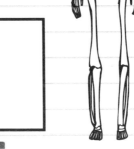

SCIENCE: More true or false?

1. Bronchitis is an inflammation of the passageways of the lungs.

☑ ☐   ☐ ☒

2. The heart produces insulin, which helps to process sugar.

☑ ☐   ☐ ☒

3. The gyratory system carries blood around the body.

☑ ☐   ☐ ☒

4. Diabetes is a common condition that means the human body cannot regulate blood sugar levels effectively.

☑ ☐   ☐ ☒

5. In the human body, the three main types of blood vessels are capillaries, arteries and veins.

☑ ☐   ☐ ☒

6. The eight front teeth in the adult human mouth are called inserters.

☑ ☐   ☐ ☒

7. The amount of energy in an item of food or drink is measured in ounces.

☑ ☐   ☐ ☒

8. Red is the colour of the protein haemoglobin, found in blood cells.

☑ ☐   ☐ ☒

9. Nutrients that the body needs in small amounts to function properly are called vitamins.

☑ ☐   ☐ ☒

10. The part of a tooth embedded in the jaw bone is called the root.

☑ ☐   ☐ ☒

SCIENCE: Living things

1. **The adjective 'feline' refers to what type of domesticated animal?**

a) cat
b) dog
c) hamster

2. **Dolly, the first ever mammal to be cloned from an adult cell, was which species of farmyard animal?**

a) sheep   b) cow   c) horse

3. **An Aberdeen Angus is a species of which farm animal?**

a) horse   b) cow   c) goat

4. **In the film *Finding Nemo*, what variety of fish is Nemo?**

a) clown
b) gold
c) rainbow

5. What is a baby frog called?

a) cub

b) froglet

c) kitten

6. What number do you get if you add the usual number of legs on an ant to the usual number of legs on a spider?

a) 14   b) 16   c) 12

7. Which word beginning with 'F' is the name of a type of organism that includes moulds and mushrooms?

a) fungus   b) flower   c) fruit

8. Which insect has species including Monarch, Red Admiral and Painted Lady?

a) bee   b) ladybird   c) butterfly

SCIENCE: Missing letters

1. Which word beginning with 'C' is the term for the flow of electricity around a circuit?

C _ R R _ _ _

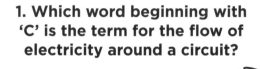

2. Fahrenheit is a unit of measurement of what property?

T _ _ _ E _ _ T _ _ _

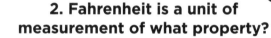

3. Which word beginning with 'P' is used to refer to the two opposite ends of a magnet?

P _ _ E S

4. In the chemical formula for carbon dioxide, CO_2, what does the 'O' stand for?

_ X _ G _ _

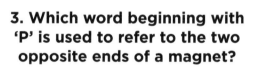

5. What 'L' is a simple lifting mechanism made from a long pole or plank and a pivot?

_ E _ E _

6. Which word beginning with 'F' is the force that occurs when an object moves against another object?

F _ _ C _ I _ _

7. The chemical formula for water is H_2O. What does the 'H' stand for?

H _ _ R _ G _ _

8. Which word beginning with 'V' can mean both a type of micro-organism that causes disease, and a malicious program that infects and damages a computer?

V _ R _ _

SCIENCE: Body word search

F	I	N	G	E	R	P	A
E	R	J	B	L	O	F	N
N	O	S	E	B	E	T	K
S	A	Q	I	O	X	G	L
L	G	D	N	W	T	W	E
K	E	E	H	C	Z	E	V
C	Y	M	A	J	H	Y	K
S	H	O	U	L	D	E	R

ANKLE
CHEEK
ELBOW
EYE
FINGER
LEG
NOSE
SHOULDER

HISTORY

HISTORY: Ancient history

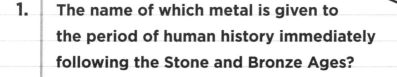

1. The name of which metal is given to the period of human history immediately following the Stone and Bronze Ages?

a) steel   b) iron   c) copper

2. In ancient Britain, the Picts used the plant woad to dye themselves which colour?

a) blue
b) red
c) green

3. Which ancient civilisation built Hadrian's Wall?

a) Vikings
b) Greeks
c) Romans

4. In Roman mythology, which twin brothers are said to have founded the city of Rome?

a) Romulus and Remus

b) Ronan and Roman

c) Reeves and Resus

5. Rulers of which ancient empire include Nero, Tiberius and Caligula?

a) Roman

b) Greek

c) Ottoman

6. The rulers of which ancient civilisation include Hatshepsut, Ramesses II and Tutankhamun?

a) Egyptian   b) Parthian   c) Assyrian

HISTORY: Myths and legends

1. Which hero of Greek and Roman myth was said to have carried out twelve labours, including killing the Hydra?

a) Odysseus

b) Hercules

c) Icarus

2. In ancient Egyptian mythology, which organ of the body is weighed by the gods to determine your fate after death?

a) brain

b) heart

c) kidneys

3. In ancient Egypt, who was the god of the dead?

a) Anubis

b) Hades

c) Pluto

4. In Greek mythology, Gorgons are female creatures that have what animal instead of hair?

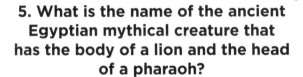

a) snakes

b) centipedes

c) worms

5. What is the name of the ancient Egyptian mythical creature that has the body of a lion and the head of a pharaoh?

a) The Minotaur

b) Griffin

c) Sphinx

6. In Norse mythology, the hammer Mjölnir belongs to which god?

a) Odin

b) Thor

c) Loki

HISTORY: Modern history

1. Which present-day European capital city was divided in two by a guarded concrete wall from 1961 until 1989?

a) Copenhagen
b) Berlin
c) Moscow

2. What was the main profession of the famous Victorian, Charles Dickens?

a) writer
b) politician
c) engineer

3. The regulations on food supply during the Second World War were known by which word beginning with 'R'?

a) relating
b) reneging
c) rationing

4. VE Day marked the end of fighting in Europe in which major war?

a) Russian Revolution
b) First World War
c) Second World War

5. The Battle of Pearl Harbor was an important conflict in which major war?

a) American Civil War

b) First World War

c) Second World War

6. Who was President of the USA immediately before Donald Trump?

a) Barack Obama

b) George W. Bush

c) Bill Clinton

7. In 1922, the archaeologist Howard Carter discovered the tomb of which Egyptian pharaoh?

a) Cleopatra

b) Tutankhamun

c) Ramesses II

8. In the Second World War, the Siege of Leningrad and the Battle of Stalingrad both took place in which country?

a) Russia

b) Poland

c) Germany

HISTORY: Travel and technology

Write the correct word into these sentences.

1. During the reign of Queen _____ , the light bulb, the telephone and the gramophone were all invented.

| Mary | Victoria | Elizabeth II |

2. Born in 1781, George _____ was a British engineer who was often called the 'Father of the Railways'.

Bernard Shaw

Stephenson

Orwell

3. The first photograph was taken in the _____ century.

| 19th | 20th | 21st |

4. In what year did the RMS *Titanic* sink?

| 1912 | 1914 | 1916 |

5. In Germany during the 15th century, Johannes _____ invented the first successful printing press.

| Pasteur | Gutenberg | Franklin |

6. The _____ War was the first major war that tanks were used in.

Boer

First World

Second World

7. The first email was sent in the _____ century.

| 19th | 20th | 21st |

HISTORY: Odd one out

Which is the odd one out in each
of these lists? Choose one and then
say why it's the odd one.

1.

Tiberius

Hatshepsut

Hadrian

_ _ _ _ _ _ _ _ _ _ _ _ _

_ _ _ _ _ _ _ _ _ _ _ _ _

_ _ _ _ _ _ _ _ _ _ _ _ _

_ _ _ _ _ _ _ _ _ _ _ _ _

2.

_ _ _ _ _ _ _ _ _ _ _ _ _

_ _ _ _ _ _ _ _ _ _ _ _ _

_ _ _ _ _ _ _ _ _ _ _ _ _

_ _ _ _ _ _ _ _ _ _ _ _ _

Ming

Shang

Meiji

3.

Zeus

Thor

Loki

_ _ _ _ _ _ _ _ _ _ _ _ _

_ _ _ _ _ _ _ _ _ _ _ _ _

_ _ _ _ _ _ _ _ _ _ _ _ _

_ _ _ _ _ _ _ _ _ _ _ _ _

4.

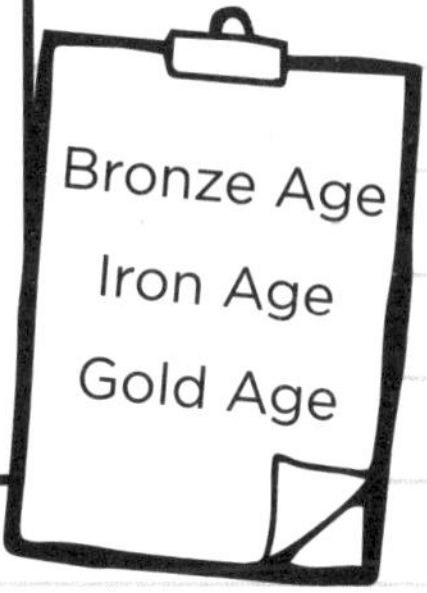

_____
_____
_____
_____
_____

Bronze Age
Iron Age
Gold Age

5.

_____
_____
_____
_____
_____

Hadrian's Wall, UK
Colosseum, Rome
Acropolis, Athens

6.

_____
_____
_____
_____
_____

Great Ziggurat of Ur
Great Pyramid of Giza
Temple of Luxor

HISTORY: Ancient Egypt

1. **As well as the Great Pyramids, the ancient Egyptian monuments at Giza include an enormous sculpture of a mythological creature called a Sphinx. Pick the correct description of it below.**

   a) The body of a lion and the head of a pharaoh
   b) The body of a serpent and the head of a jackal
   c) The body of a hippopotamus and the head of a crocodile

2. **In ancient Egyptian mythology, Anuket was the goddess of which river?**

   a) the Danube
   b) the Nile
   c) the Zambezi

3. Who was the ruler of ancient Egypt when it fell to the Roman Empire?

a) Tutankhamun
b) Cleopatra
c) Ramesses III

4. What is the name given to the Egyptian valley where powerful nobles and leaders were buried?

a) the Valley of the Pharaohs
b) the Valley of the Kings
c) the Valley of the Nile

5. Which ancient Egyptian queen was married to the pharaoh Akhenaten?

a) Nefertiti   b) Cleopatra   c) Hatshepsut

1. In Greek mythology, Gorgons are female creatures that can turn you to what if you look at them?

    a) silver

    b) stone

    c) gold

2. In Greek mythology, how many heads does Hades's guard dog Cerberus have?

    a) eight

    b) five

    c) three

3. The capital city of Greece is named after which ancient goddess?

    a) Aphrodite

    b) Athena

    c) Persephone

4. Often referred to as 'the father of science', which Greek philosopher founded the Lyceum, an ancient institute of education?

a) Sophocles

b) Aristotle

c) Heraclitus

5. Athens was defeated by which other city-state during the Peloponnesian War?

a) Sparta

b) Memphis

c) Rome

6. What is the word used to describe an ancient Greek settlement or citadel?

a) Acropolis

b) Hypothesis

c) Parthenon

HISTORY: Ancient Rome

1. **The ancient Roman city of Pompeii was destroyed by an eruption of which volcano?**

> a) Popocatépetl
>
> b) Etna
>
> c) Vesuvius

2. **Which of these is the Latin name for a capital city in the United Kingdom?**

> a) Eboracum
>
> b) Londinium
>
> c) Lutetia

3. **Which letters did the Romans use to represent the numbers 5 and 1000?**

> a) C and M
>
> b) L and C
>
> c) V and M

4. Who of the following was not a Roman Emperor?

> a) Claudius
> b) Nero
> c) Virgil

5. What is the name of the largest amphitheatre built in Rome, which hosted events, such as gladiator battles?

> a) The Forum
> b) The Pantheon
> c) The Colosseum

6. What name was given to Roman army officers who commanded approximately 100 men?

> a) caesars
> b) centurions
> c) legionaries

HISTORY: Brave new worlds

1. Christopher Columbus's first expedition to the Americas began from which European country?

a) Spain
b) England
c) Italy

2. Which explorer sailed to Australia and New Zealand on the ship HMS *Endeavour*?

a) James Cook
b) James Kirk
c) James Cookson

3. In the 16th century, who was the first explorer to circumnavigate the world?

a) Fergus Magellore
b) Ferdinand Magellan
c) Furry Magalud

4. Who was the first woman to fly solo across the Atlantic?

a) Amelia Braveheart
b) Amelia Eyeheart
c) Amelia Earhart

5. Who was the first man on the Moon?

a) Buzz Aldrin
b) Michael Collins
c) Neil Armstrong

6. The Niña, Pinta and Santa María were the ships of which 15th-century explorer?

a) Christopher Columbus
b) Christopher Robin
c) Christopher Reeves

7. Who was the first woman to travel around the world in 72 days?

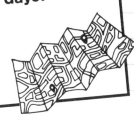

a) Nellie Bly
b) Nellie Sly
c) Nellie Wry

**1. Which war began on
1 September, 1939?**

a) First World War
b) Second World War
c) Crimean War

**2. What is celebrated on
4 July in the USA?**

a) Independence Day
b) Martin Luther King Jr Day
c) United Nations Day

**3. What is celebrated every year on
14 July in France?**

a) Bastille Day
b) Baguette day
c) Louis Day

4. Which war started on 28 July, 1914?

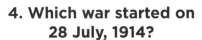

    a) First World War
    b) Second World War
    c) Crimean War

5. What revolution took place during the years 1775-1783?

    a) American Revolution
    b) French Revolution
    c) Russian Revolution

6. When was the building of the Eiffel Tower completed?

    a) 1889
    b) 1959
    c) 1909

HISTORY: Inventions

1. **When did the Wright brothers famously fly their first aircraft?**

a) 1903   a) 1803   a) 1953

2. **Who invented the first motor car?**

a) Henry Ford
b) Karl Benz
c) Audi Quattro

3. **Who invented the telephone in 1876?**

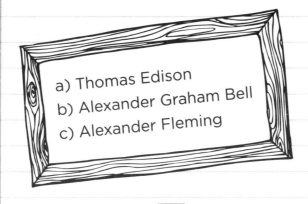

a) Thomas Edison
b) Alexander Graham Bell
c) Alexander Fleming

4. **Who discovered penicillin?**

a) Alexander Fleming

b) Alexander Graham Bell

c) Alexander Armstrong

5. **Who invented the ballpoint pen?**

a) Ladislao and Georg Biro

b) Ellen and Noel Ball

c) Roger Highlight

6. **Who discovered two elements and won two Nobel Prizes?**

a) Marie Curie
b) Marie Antoinette
c) Marie Marvingt

HISTORY: Modern history alphabet

The answers in this section begin with the letter given at the beginning of the question.

A The first woman to fly solo from Britain to Australia was _____ Johnson.

. . . .

B The Somme, Stalingrad, Trafalgar and Waterloo are all names of famous _____.

. . . .

C Which famous explorer discovered Cuba in 1492?

. . . .

D What type of mammal was Laika (pron. Lie-kah), the first animal to orbit the Earth?

. . . .

E In which country was the first public railway line? It ran 40 km from Stockton to Darlington.

. . . .

F In the First World War, the Battles of the Marne and the Somme both took place in this country.

. . . .

G _____ Washington is regarded as the first president of the USA.

. . . .

H Which English king famously had six wives?

. . . .

I The RMS *Titanic* was built in Northern _____, part of the UK.

. . . .

J _____ and Guernsey are two of the Channel Islands that were occupied by Germany during the Second World War.

. . . .

K This 'K' is the middle name of the British engineer Isambard _____ Brunel, considered an important figure in the Industrial Revolution. The same word also means a country ruled by a king or queen.

. . . .

L In the Second World War, the 'blackout' was when you had to make sure no _____ could be seen.

. . . .

M Angela _____ became the Chancellor of Germany in 2005.

. . . .

N In which month did Germany sign the first agreement for peace (the Armistice) with Britain and France at the end of the First World War?

. . . .

O What was the code name for Nazi Germany's proposed invasion of Britain during the Second World War?

. . . .

P This is the name of the harbour in the USA that was attacked by Japanese bombers in 1941. This attack led to the USA's entry into the Second World War.

. . . .

Q On 9 September, 2015, who became the world's longest-reigning monarch?

. . . .

R _____ Amundsen was an explorer who led the expedition to be the first people to reach the South Pole.

. . . .

S VE Day marked the end of fighting in Europe in which major war?

. . . .

T Which fearsome armoured vehicle was first used in battle in the First World War?

. . . .

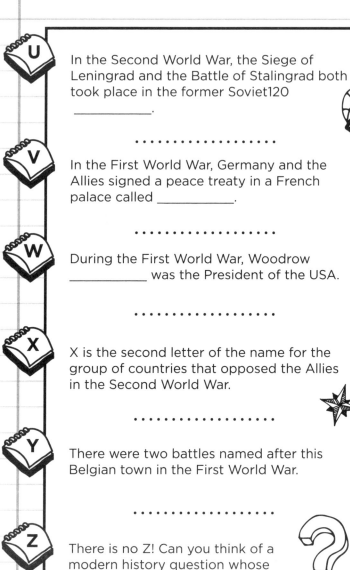

U In the Second World War, the Siege of Leningrad and the Battle of Stalingrad both took place in the former Soviet120

_____.

· · · · · · · · · · · · · · · · · · ·

V In the First World War, Germany and the Allies signed a peace treaty in a French palace called _____.

· · · · · · · · · · · · · · · · · · ·

W During the First World War, Woodrow _____ was the President of the USA.

· · · · · · · · · · · · · · · · · · ·

X X is the second letter of the name for the group of countries that opposed the Allies in the Second World War.

· · · · · · · · · · · · · · · · · · ·

Y There were two battles named after this Belgian town in the First World War.

· · · · · · · · · · · · · · · · · · ·

Z There is no Z! Can you think of a modern history question whose answer begins with Z?

· · · · · · · · · · · · · · · · · · ·

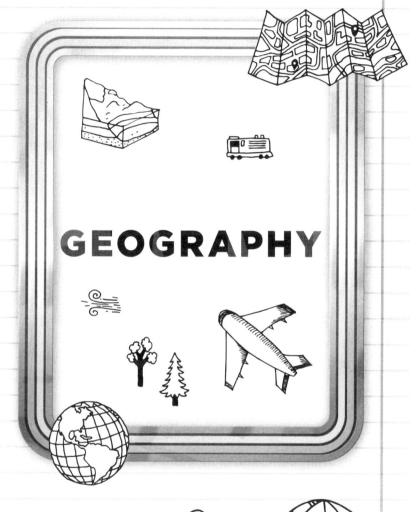

GEOGRAPHY

GEOGRAPHY: Cities around the world

1. Osaka, Kyoto and Hiroshima are all cities in which Asian country?

    a) China

    b) Japan

    c) South Korea

2. Valencia and Seville are cities in which European country?

    a) France

    b) Portugal

    c) Spain

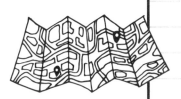

3. Tower Bridge and Piccadilly Circus are famous landmarks in which UK city?

    a) Birmingham

    b) London

    c) Manchester

4. Florence, Naples and Venice are all cities in which European country?

    a) Italy
    b) Greece
    c) Switzerland

5. Melbourne and Canberra are cities located in which country?

    a) South Africa
    b) Australia
    c) New Zealand

6. In which European country are the cities of Marseille and Lyon?

    a) France
    b) Germany
    c) Belgium

GEOGRAPHY: Capital cities

☑ True or false? ✗

1. Moscow is the capital of Poland.

☑ ☐   ☐ ✗

2. Tokyo is the capital city of Japan.

☑ ☐   ☐ ✗

3. Cairo is the capital city of Algeria.

☑ ☐   ☐ ✗

4. Budapest is the capital city of Romania.

☑ ☐   ☐ ✗

**5. The names of the capital cities
of Belgium and Germany both begin
with the letter 'M'.**

☑ ☐   ☐ ✗

6. The Louvre Museum is located in the capital city of Spain, Madrid.

☑ ☐   ☐ ☒

7. Oslo is the capital city of Norway.

☑ ☐   ☐ ☒

8. Guadalajara is the capital city of Mexico.

☑ ☐   ☐ ☒

9. The world famous 'Little Mermaid' statue is located by the harbour in Copenhagen, the capital of Denmark.

☑ ☐   ☐ ☒

10. Lima is the capital of Peru.

☑ ☐   ☐ ☒

GEOGRAPHY: Flags

> **Write the correct word into these sentences.**

1. The national flag of China features five yellow stars on a _____ background.

red
blue
green

2.

blue
green
orange

The national flags of Chile, the Czech Republic and Russia are made up of red, _____ and white.

3. The flag of _____ has an eagle holding a snake in its centre.

Ivory Coast   Mexico   Australia

4. The national flag of Iceland has _____ colours on it.

 1   2   3

5. The national flags of Finland and Greece are made up of _____ and blue.

red
white
green

6. The national flag of Poland features _____ colours.

 2  3   4

7. The cross on the national flag of Switzerland is _____ .

white   red   blue

GEOGRAPHY: Physical geography

1. **What name is given to volcanic magma once it reaches the surface of the Earth?**

> a) ash   b) lava   c) sediment

2. **Which imaginary lines circle the earth vertically at regular intervals?**

> a) longitude
> b) latitude
> c) tropics

3. **Which of the world's oceans is the largest?**

> a) Atlantic
> b) Indian
> c) Pacific

4. The Andes mountain range can be found on which continent?

a) North America
b) South America
c) Asia

5. In what type of natural geographical feature would you typically find a meander?

a) mountain   b) river   c) ocean

6. What is the name of the active volcano in Sicily?

a) Etna   b) Edna   c) Elvis

1. The US state of Hawaii is surrounded by which body of water?

a) Atlantic Ocean
b) Pacific Ocean
c) Caribbean Sea

2. Lake Superior and Lake Ontario lie on the border between the USA and which other country?

a) Mexico
b) Canada
c) Cuba

3. The US states of New York and Florida both have a coastline on which body of water?

a) Atlantic Ocean
b) Pacific Ocean
c) Caribbean Sea

4. In which US state are the cities of San Francisco and Los Angeles?

a) Colorado

b) Connecticut

c) California

5. Which word can go before 'Hampshire', 'Jersey' and 'York' to make the names of three US states?

a) South

b) Greater

c) New

6. Which is the largest US state by population?

a) New York

b) California

c) Texas

GEOGRAPHY: Countries

1. If I start in Oslo, and travel directly east in a straight line, which other country will I come to first?

a) Sweden
b) Finland
c) Denmark

2. In which country is John F. Kennedy International Airport located?

a) Canada
b) USA
c) United Kingdom

3. Which continent is India part of?

a) North America
b) Asia
c) Europe

4. The USA states of Arizona and Texas both border which other country?

a) Canada
b) Mexico
c) Bolivia

5. Which country in Europe shares its border with nine other countries?

a) Germany

b) Italy

c) Spain

6. Which country has provinces called Nova Scotia, Saskatchewan and British Columbia?

a) USA

b) Canada

c) Russia

7. Which European country has regions called Galicia and Andalusia?

a) Portugal

b) Spain

c) France

8. In which country is the Sydney Harbour Bridge, opened in 1932?

a) Australia

b) China

c) USA

GEOGRAPHY: Countries

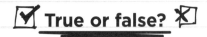 True or false?

1. There is only one country in South America that begins with the letter 'U'.

2. The country of Paraguay is located on the continent of Africa.

3. The Netherlands and Germany are the only countries to share a land border with Denmark.

4. The country of Botswana is located on the continent of Africa.

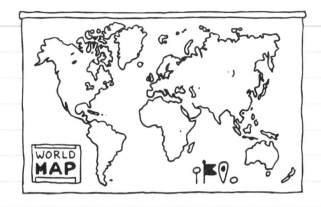

5. Spain is the only country that shares a land border with Portugal.

☑ ☐   ☐ ☒

6. San Marino is a country in South America.

☑ ☐   ☐ ☒

7. Myanmar and Mongolia are in Australasia.

☑ ☐   ☐ ☒

8. São Paulo and Rio de Janeiro are major cities in Argentina.

☑ ☐   ☐ ☒

GEOGRAPHY: Hidden monument

Solve the clues and write the answers in the boxes.

1. The capital of Japan.

2. This river runs through London.

3. This capital in the Middle East is important in three faiths: Judaism, Islam and Christianity.

4. This capital city used to be called Saigon.

5. This South American country sits between Argentina, Brazil and Bolivia.

6. This Japanese city was struck by an atomic bomb in 1945.

7. North Cape is in the far north of this country.

8. The capital of Peru.

When you have done them all, you will find the name of a very popular tourist monument in India in the shaded squares.

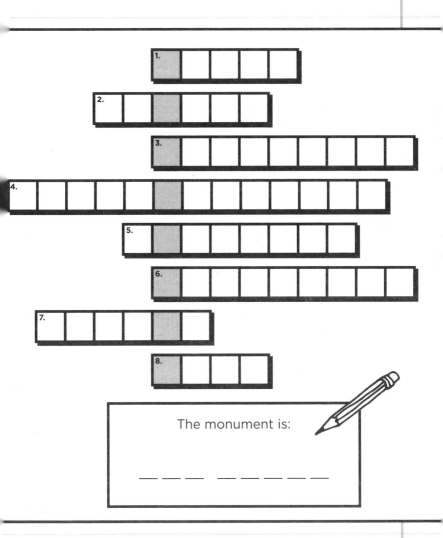

1.

2.

3.

4.

5.

6.

7.

8.

The monument is:

_ _ _ _   _ _ _ _ _

1. What is the second largest city in the United Kingdom by population?

    a) Birmingham
    b) Portsmouth
    c) Belfast

2. Which Scottish city contains The Royal Mile, a succession of streets that lead up to the city's castle gates?

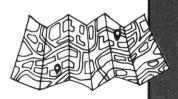

    a) Glasgow
    b) Dundee
    c) Edinburgh

3. What is the name given to the geographical area in the east of England comprising of the counties Norfolk, Suffolk and Cambridgeshire?

    a) East Tyneside
    b) East Anglia
    c) East Moors

4. What is the longest river in the UK?

a) The Thames
b) The Severn
c) The Trent

5. What is the deepest body of water in the UK?

a) Lake Windermere
b) Loch Morar
c) Lough Neagh

6. The Brecon Beacons mountain range is in which UK country?

a) Northern Ireland
b) Scotland
c) Wales

GEOGRAPHY: Confused capitals

To find the answers, un-jumble the letters written below each question.

1. The famous Louvre museum is in this capital city.

APRIS

_ _ _ _ _

2. The capital city of a Scandinavian country.

TSKCHLMOO

_ _ _ _ _ _ _ _ _

3. The River Danube flows through this capital of a Central European country.

BPDTSUAE

_ _ _ _ _ _ _ _

4. The 'Little Mermaid' statue sits by the harbour of this capital.

P C E E N A G N O H

_ _ _ _ _ _ _ _ _ _

5. The capital of Egypt.

I A O C R

_ _ _ _ _

6. The Kremlin is the historic centre of this city.

O S O M W C

_ _ _ _ _ _

GEOGRAPHY: Australia and New Zealand

1. What is the northernmost city of Australia?

a) Perth

b) Sydney

c) Darwin

2. Also known as Ayers Rock, what is the official name of the large sandstone rock formation in central Australia?

a) Kata Tjuta

b) Uluru

c) Mount Kosciuszko

3. Which country is Australia's closest geographical neighbour?

a) Papua New Guinea

b) New Zealand

c) Indonesia

4. What is the name of the sea that separates Australia and New Zealand?

a) Coral Sea

b) Timor Sea
c) Tasman Sea

5. Found in the caldera of a supervolcano, what is the name of the largest lake in New Zealand?

a) Lake Rotorua

b) Lake Taupo
c) Lake Wanaka

6. What is the name of the mountain range that runs down the west coast of New Zealand's South Island?

a) Southern Alps
b) Southern Beacons

c) Southern Andes

GEOGRAPHY: Match the cities

Match three of the cities in the right-hand column to each country in the left-hand column.

JAPAN . . . .

. . . .

. . . .

SPAIN . . . .

. . . .

. . . .

ITALY . . . .

. . . .

. . . .

AUSTRALIA . . . .

. . . .

. . . .

CANADA . . . .

. . . .

. . . .

INDIA . . . .

. . . .

. . . .

Osaka

Seville

Naples

Mumbai

Melbourne

Valencia

Kolkata

Venice

Canberra

Kyoto

Vancouver

Montreal

Delhi

Barcelona

Fukushima

Florence

Perth

Ottawa

GEOGRAPHY: More flags

Match the countries to the descriptions of their flags. Read the questions carefully – sometimes you need to find more than one country. You can only use the names of countries in the box below for your answers.

Norway   Australia

                            New Zealand

Romania   Greece

Finland   Iceland

1

Which two Nordic countries have flags that are red, white and blue and look very similar? One has a blue background with a red cross or white; the other has a red background with a blue cross on white.

_____ _____

2

These two countries feature only blue and white on their flags.

_____ _____

3

The flag of this country has three vertical stripes. Starting from the flagpole, the stripes are blue, yellow and red.

_____

4

The flags of which two countries feature both a small Union Flag and the Southern Cross star constellation?

_____

_____

GEOGRAPHY: Missing letters

1. **The magnitude of earthquakes is measured using this scale:**

R _ _ H _ _ R

2. **The large, shifting pieces that make up the Earth's crust are referred to as:**

TECTONIC P _ _ T _ _

3. **The name of a large natural or artificial lake used as a source of water supply:**

_ ES _ R _ O _ R

4. **A river or stream that flows into a larger river or lake:**

T _ I _ _ T _ _ Y

5. **The season of heavy rain during the summer in hot Asian countries:**

_ O _ _ O _ N

6. What type of cloud is most associated with thunderstorms?

C _ M U _ _ N _ _ B _ S

7. Imaginary lines that circle the Earth vertically at regular intervals:

LINES OF L _ N _ _ T _ _ E

8. The largest island in the world:

G _ _ _ N _ A _ D

9. A huge, moving body of ice and snow:

_ _ A _ _ N _ HE

10. The Great Barrier Reef is located off the northeast coast of which country:

_ U _ _ RA_I_

GEOGRAPHY: Missing places

Complete the sentences using the correct answer.

1. The country of Chile is located on the continent of _____ .

South America

Africa

North America

2. Stockholm is the capital city of _____ .

| Norway | Denmark | Sweden |

3. Madrid is the capital of _____.

| Spain | Germany | Netherlands |

4. Kenya is located on the continent of

_____ .

| Africa | Europe | Antarctica |

5. The island of Ibiza belongs to

_____ .

| Italy | Tunisia | Spain |

6. Lima is the capital city of _____ .

| Mexico

Guatemala

Peru |

7. São Paulo and Rio de Janeiro are major cities in the country of _____ .

| Chile | Argentina | Brazil |

GEOGRAPHY: Starting with 'S'

The answers to all these questions begin with the letter 'S'.

1. This landlocked country has borders with Italy, France, Germany and Austria.

. . . .

2. A word you can put before 'Korea' and 'Africa' to make the names of two countries.

. . . .

3. A common collective name for the countries of Norway, Sweden and Denmark.

. . . .

4. The S_____ Harbour Bridge is in a city on the east coast of Australia.

. . . .

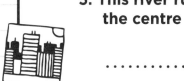

5. This river runs through the centre of Paris.

. . . .

6. Uruguay is a country in this continent.

. . . .

7. This tiny republic is surrounded on all sides by Italy.

. . . .

8. This island in the Mediterranean sea lies south of Corsica and belongs to Italy.

. . . .

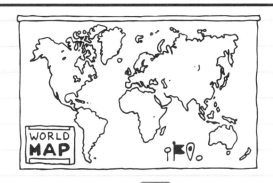

GEOGRAPHY: True or false?

1. The didgeridoo is a large marsupial that lives in Australia.

 ☑ ☐   ☐ ☒

2. The nickname for New York is 'The Big Apple'.

 ☑ ☐   ☐ ☒

3. Myanmar and Mongolia are both countries in Asia.

☑ ☐   ☐ ☒

4. San Francisco and Chicago are major cities in Chile.

☑ ☐   ☐ ☒

5. Minnesota, Pennsylvania and Montana are all provinces in Australia.

6. Big Ben and Trafalgar Square are famous landmarks in Manchester, UK.

7. Helsinki is the capital city of Finland.

8. The capital of Peru is Cuzco.

GEOGRAPHY: Mix-up

These questions are a mix of different aspects of geography. Can you answer them all?

1 What is the capital city of China?

_____

2 Name the mountain range that separates France and Spain.

_____

3 Which is the largest ocean?

_____

4 What do you call a winding curve, or loop, in the middle or lower course of a river?

_____

5 What became the capital city of Australia in 1927?

_____

6 Can you name three countries the River Amazon flows through?

_____   _____

_____

7 What is the name of the part of a river that is formed by sediment deposits near where the river enters the sea?

_____

GEOGRAPHY: European countries

F	E	C	N	A	R	F	L
L	N	P	O	L	A	N	D
Q	S	I	R	G	K	I	G
A	E	P	W	D	S	T	R
H	S	L	A	R	N	A	E
R	M	J	Y	I	Z	L	E
G	E	R	M	A	N	Y	C
B	N	E	D	E	W	S	E

FRANCE
POLAND
SPAIN
GERMANY
SWEDEN
GREECE
ITALY
NORWAY

GEOGRAPHY: Mountains crossword

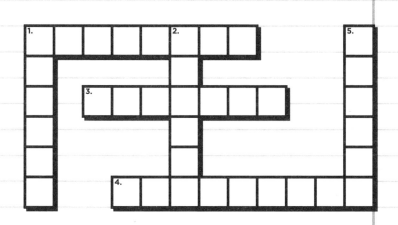

CLUES:

Across

1. In which country of the UK is the mountain Ben Nevis?

3. What is the name of the highest mountain above sea-level in the world?

4. What word means a sudden slide of snow, ice and rocks down a mountain?

Down

1. Which word is used to mean the highest point of a mountain?

2. On which continent is Mount Kilimanjaro?

5. Mont Blanc is on the border between Italy and which other country?

GEOGRAPHY: Weather word search

R	A	I	N	G	Z	C	O
K	T	P	N	N	T	U	N
F	O	U	G	R	E	Y	C
D	S	N	O	W	E	I	L
A	J	H	F	V	L	B	O
Q	X	A	S	M	S	F	U
B	L	I	Z	Z	A	R	D
E	W	L	B	U	L	T	H

RAIN
SUN
FOG
SNOW
BLIZZARD
CLOUD
HAIL
SLEET

TEST THE TEACHER

TEST THE TEACHER: Books

1. In the *Harry Potter* series, what is the name of the only entirely wizarding village in Britain?

a) Hogwards

b) Hogsmeade

c) Diagon Alley

2. What is the name of Hiccup's dragon in *How To Train Your Dragon*?

a) Toothless

b) Astrid

c) Valka

3. Which fictional vegetable does the BFG eat?

a) Snozzcumber

b) Bananagram

c) Melonia

4. In the *Harry Potter* books, which character's middle names are Percival Wulfric Brian?

a) Ron Weasley
b) Albus Dumbledore
c) Hermione Granger

5. Batman, Superman, Wonder Woman and Green Lantern are members of the Justice ... what?

a) Squad
b) Team
c) League

6. Which of these is NOT a real title of a David Walliams book?

a) *Gangsta Granny*
b) *Ratburger*
c) *Billionaire Girl*

TEST THE TEACHER: Film

1. **Lightning McQueen is a character in which series of animated films?**

a) *Toy Story*
b) *Cars*
c) *Incredibles*

2. **In the *Star Wars* film series, what is the name of Han and Leia's son?**

a) Luke Skywalker
b) Kylo Ren
c) Finn

3. **Captain Jack Sparrow is a character in which film series?**

a) *Pirates of the Caribbean*
b) *The Avengers*
c) *Transformers*

4. **The minions first appeared in which animated film?**

a) *Minions*
b) *Shrek*
c) *Despicable Me*

5. The term 'animé' refers to animation from or in the style of which country?

a) China
b) South Korea
c) Japan

6. In the Marvel films, what is the real name of Iron Man?

a) Steve Rogers
b) Tony Stark
c) Bruce Banner

7. In Transformers, which robot is the leader of the Autobots?

a) Optimus Prime
b) Bumblebee
c) Megatron

8. In the film Frozen, what is the name of Kristoff's reindeer?

a) Olaf
b) Marshmallow
c) Sven

TEST THE TEACHER: Music

1. **Which singer refers to her fan base as the 'KatyCats'?**

a) KT Tunstall
b) Katy Perry
c) Kate Nash

2. **Which singer's fan base is known as the 'Bey Hive'?**

a) Solange
b) Beyoncé
c) Taylor Swift

3. **Who is the oldest of the original members of One Direction?**

a) Louis Tomlinson
b) Zayn Malik
c) Niall Horan

4. The pop star Sia was born in which country?

a) New Zealand   b) Canada   c) Australia

5. Chris Martin is the lead singer of which famous band?

a) Muse   b) Coldplay   c) The 1975

6. What is the stage name of New Zealand-born popstar Ella Yelich-O'Connor?

a) Lorde   b) Lady Gaga   c) Dua Lipa

7. Taylor Swift's fifth album was named after what year?

a) 1975   b) 1989   c) 2001

TEST THE TEACHER: Gaming

1. The *Skylanders* character Spyro the Dragon is mainly which colour?

    a) blue
    b) green
    c) purple

2. Which Nintendo character is the star of the game *Woolly World*?

    a) Mario
    b) Yoshi
    c) Kirby

3. Flareon (pr. flare-ee-on) is an evolved form of which Pokémon?

    a) Eevee
    b) Pikachu
    c) Squirtle

4. Wigglytuff is the evolved form of which Pokémon?

   a) Ditto
   b) Jigglypuff
   c) Gengar

5. In video games, the abbreviation 'EXP' is short for which two words?

   a) experienced player
   b) experience points
   c) exponential points

6. Epic Games developed which hit computer game beginning with F?

   a) *Final Fantasy*
   b) *Fortnite*
   c) *Fable*

TEST THE TEACHER: Tech

1. What 'S' is the name of the electronics company that developed the PlayStation console?

a) Sony
b) Samsung
c) Sennheiser

2. What 'M' is the name of the technology company that developed the Xbox games console?

a) Minotaur
b) Microsoft
c) Mitre

3. In computing, the abbreviation 'ROM' stands for 'Read-Only ... what?'

a) memory
b) machine
c) mac

4. In electronics, what does the letter 'L' stand for in the abbreviation 'L.E.D'?

a) length
b) latitude
c) light

5. What 'T' is the name for a small portable computer that uses a touch-screen rather than a keyboard?

a) Toshiba

b) table-top PC

c) tablet

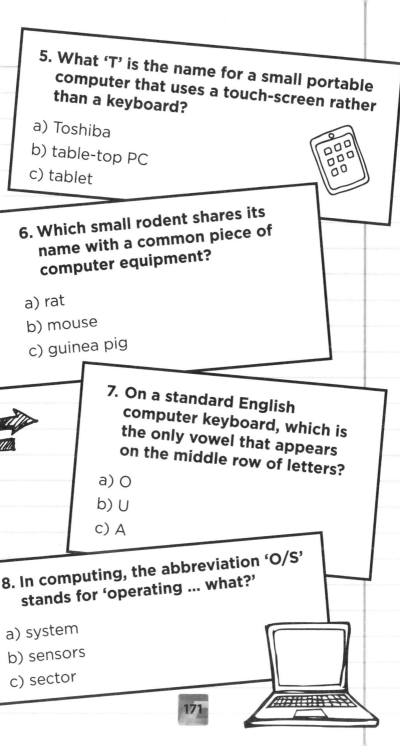

6. Which small rodent shares its name with a common piece of computer equipment?

a) rat

b) mouse

c) guinea pig

7. On a standard English computer keyboard, which is the only vowel that appears on the middle row of letters?

a) O

b) U

c) A

8. In computing, the abbreviation 'O/S' stands for 'operating ... what?'

a) system

b) sensors

c) sector

TEST THE TEACHER: Sport

1. **What nationality is the tennis player Novak Djokovic?**

a) Russian   b) Serbian   c) Croatian

2. **In skateboarding, a wheelie is known by which word beginning with 'M'?**

a) manual   b) manhattan   c) manufacture

3. **'El Clásico' is a nickname given to a football match played by Real Madrid and which other club?**

a) Atlético Madrid
b) Barcelona
c) Valencia

4.

a) Rome
b) Turin
c) Milan

In which Italian city is the San Siro Stadium located?

5. Which 'O' is a jump in skateboarding made without the use of a ramp?

a) over jump

b) ollie

c) onside kick

6. What nationality is the football player Cristiano Ronaldo?

a) Portuguese

b) Spanish

c) Brazilian

7. Which British racing driver has won the Formula 1 Championship the most times?

a) Damon Hill

b) Jensen Button

c) Lewis Hamilton

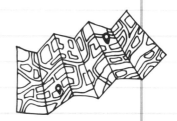

TEST THE TEACHER: Fashion

1. Ray-Ban Aviators are a style of which type of accessory?

    a) belt

    b) watch

    c) sunglasses

2. What 'J' is a one-piece garment that is trousers and a long-sleeved top stitched together?

    a) jumpsuit

    b) jeggings

    c) jeans

3. 'Lariat' is a variety of which item of jewellery?

    a) bracelet

    b) earring

    c) necklace

4. Which rapper designed the Yeezy trainer range?

    a) Chance the Rapper
    b) Kanye West
    c) Kendrick Lemar

5. What is the name of Beyoncé's fashion label?

    a) Ivy Park
    b) Gold Park
    c) Black and Yellow

6. In what city is the Met Gala hosted?

    a) Paris
    b) Milan
    c) New York

TEST THE TEACHER: Text abbreviations

1. The text abbreviation SMH usually stands for 'Shaking my...' what?

a) hand
b) head
c) hips

2. The text abbreviation TFW usually stands for 'That...what'?

a) feel when
b) fight when
c) flight when

3. What does the text abbreviation IDGI stand for?

a) I don't grow it
b) I deeply get it
c) I don't get it

4. What does the text abbreviation 'LOL' stand for?

a) lots of love
b) laugh out loud
c) laugh of love

5. What does the text abbreviation IKR stand for?

a) I know right
b) I knew really
c) I know rhymes

6. What does the text abbreviation BRB stand for?

a) be really brainy
b) be right back
c) be really bold

7. What does the text abbreviation FTW stand for?

a) for the weekend
b) for the win
c) for the web

8. What does the text abbreviation TMI stand for?

a) too much information
b) tell me instead
c) thank me instead

TEST THE TEACHER: TV

1. **SpongeBob SquarePants lives in what type of fruit under the sea?**

a) pineapple   b) apple   c) mango

2. **In the TV show *Friends*, who is the manager of the coffee shop Central Perk?**

a) Gunther   b) Ross   c) Monica

3. **In the TV show *The Simpsons*, who is the father of Rod and Todd?**

a) Kirk Van Houten
b) Ned Flanders
c) Clancy Wiggum

4. **Finn and Jake are the heroes of which animated TV show?**

a) *Adventure Time*
b) *Steven Universe*
c) *Over the Garden Wall*

ANSWERS

ENGLISH

Opposites: p10–11

1. a) interior; 2. a) innocent;
3. b) senior; 4. b) horizontal;
5. c) maximum; 6. a) private

Poetry: p12–13

1. a) personification;
2. c) alliteration; 3. b) simile;
4. b) metre; 5. b) poem

Punctuation: p14–15

1. a) ellipsis; 2. a) question mark; 3. b) full stop; 4. c) The man's hat blew off in the strong wind. 5. c) Fred and George had to get to Saint Edward's school by eight o'clock. 6. b) a quote mark; 7. b) semicolon; 8.a) It links two words together.

Grammar: True or false?: p16–17

1. True; 2. False; 3. True;
4. False; 5. False; 6. True;
7. True; 8. False; 9. False;
10. True

Spelling: Circle the correct words: p18

1. courageous; 2. rhythm; 3. solemn; 4. receive;
5. accommodate;
6. embarrass

Spelling: Names of flowers: p19

Daisy; Daffodil; Thistle; Violet

Missing words: p20–21

1. jumped; 2. quicker;
3. buzzing; 4. caught;
5. there; 6. whole; 7. sent

Word search: p22

P	T	E	N	S	E	N	S
R	P	X	A	H	O	S	U
A	R	E	N	O	U	N	F
D	E	X	E	M	I	F	F
V	F	F	W	O	R	D	I
E	I	L	T	N	O	R	X
R	X	S	R	Y	E	O	L
B	O	N	M	M	R	N	E

Word formation: p23

1. house; 2. super; 3. board

Homophones: p24

1. tail; 2. bored;

180

3. wear; 4. alter; 5. whether;
6. threw; 7. week; 8. cereal

Grammar crossword: p25

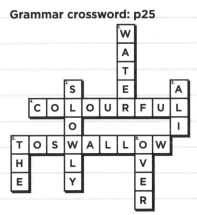

More spelling: p26-27

1. preferred; 2. poisonous; 3. neighbour; 4. prejudice; 5. communicate; 6. cemetery; 7. forty; 8. awkward; 9. disastrous; 10. symbol; 11. committee; 12. conscious; 13. aggressive; 14. dictionary; 15. exaggerate; 16. sincerely

More missing words: p28-29

1. stationery; 2. weary; 3. morning; 4. herd; 5. advice; 6. practise, practice; 7. aisle

Word jumbles: p30-31

1. palindrome; 2. narrator; 3. onomatopoeia; 4. author; 5. thesaurus; 6. fiction; 7. dictionary; 8. metaphor

Word search: p32

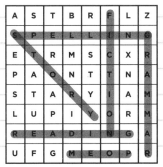

MATHS

Shapes: p34-35

1. b) six
2. a) quadrilateral
3. c) cylinder
4. b) equilateral
5. b) 12 centimetres
6. a) 40
7. b) 24
8. a) 4

True or false?: p36

1. False; 2. True; 3. True;

4. False; 5. False; 6. True

prime; 6. 64; 7. 13

Shapes word search: p37

B	G	C	E	N	O	C	H
T	R	I	A	N	G	L	E
E	M	R	L	H	Q	B	X
O	S	C	Y	B	U	R	A
V	Z	L	F	C	J	N	G
A	P	E	I	X	Y	K	O
L	S	Q	U	A	R	E	N
S	U	B	M	O	H	R	A

Angles: p38–39

1. b) 90 degrees

2. a) acute

3. a) protractor

4. c) south-east

5. a) 50 degrees

6. c) perpendicular

Measurements: p40–41

1. b) 13; 2. a) 100; 3. b) 500;

4. c) 200; 5. b) 250;

6. b) 1,000; 7. c) 1,000

Fractions: p42–43

1. c) numerator; 2. a) 1/4; 3.

b) 12; 4. a) 1/12; 5. b) 1/10; 6.

c) 3/4 ; 7. 5/8; 8. 0.8; 9. 5/6

Numbers: p44–45

1. 25; 2. 36; 3. 9; 4. 12; 5.

Problems: p46–47

1. b) 60%; 2. b) 20%;

3. a) 1:4; 4. b) 1/2; 5. b)

2; 6. c) 105;

7. a = 65 degrees

Sequences: p48–49

1. a) 148; b) 243; c) 78; d) 83;

e) 30; f) 35; g) 30; h) 63

2. 99; 3. 12; 4. 10.25; 5. 30; 6.

144; 7. 352

Work it out: p50–51

1. 20; 2. 180 degrees; 3. 200

grams; 4. 10; 5. 40; 6. 0.25;

7. 25; 8. subtraction; 9. 4

Missing letters: p52–53

1. chord; 2. venn; 3. mean; 4.

pie; 5. digit; 6. denominator;

7. circumference

More shapes: p54–55

1. isosceles; 2. parallelogram;

3. trapezium; 4. kite;

5. heptagon; 6. octagon

Roman numerals: p56–57

1. b) M; 2. c) 5; 3. a) 100;

4. b) X; 5. b) 25; 6. a) L;

7. c) 500; 8. b) 160

More problems: p58–59

1. 80%; 2. 76; 3. 33; 4. 25;

5. £1.10; 6. 31; 7. £7.80

Quick-fire: p60–62

1. 28; 2. 66; 3. 22; 4. 20; 5.

24; 6. 52; 7. 32; 8. 197; 9. 91;

10. 177; 11. 912; 12. 1038; 13.

432; 14. 49; 15. 14.8; 16. 43.5;

17. 1

SCIENCE

Human body: p64–65

1. c) white; 2. c) incisors;

3. a) tendon; 4. b) carbon

dioxide; 5. b) capillaries; 6.

b) eyes

In the mouth: p66

True or false?: p67

1. False; 2. False; 3. True;

4. False; 5. True; 6. False

Birds word search: p68

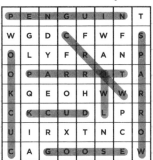

Classifying animals: p69

FUR: bear, beaver, opossum,

wolf; FEATHERS: emu,

blackbird, condor, quetzal;

SPINES: echidna, hedgehog,

sea urchin, porcupine;

SCALES: alligator, turtle,

adder, gecko

Animals: p70–71

1. c) Africa; 2. b) 16; 3. b)

beagle; 4. a) canine; 5. b)

Australia; 6. b) China; 7. c)

tail; 8. a) emu

More human body: p72–73

1. b) carbohydrates

2. a) protein

3. c) liver

4. c) iron

5. a) cavity

6. b) insulin

The planets: True or false?: p74

1. False; 2. True; 3. True; 4.
True; 5. False; 6. False

Order of the planets: p75

Mercury, Venus, Earth, Mars,
Jupiter, Saturn, Uranus,
Neptune.

Space: p76–78

1. moons; 2. telescope; 3.
gravity ; 4. constellation;
5. way; 6. comet; 7. galaxy;
8. Jupiter ; 9. Two – Mercury
and Venus; 10. comet

Space word search: p79

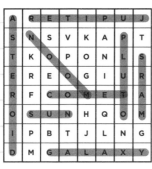

Plants: p80–81

1. b) water

2. a) nectar

3. b) pollen

4. a) oak

5. c) canopy

6. b) deciduous

7. a) nettle

Plant parts: p82–83

stamen, petals, stem, roots

1. stamen; 2. roots; 3. petals;
4. stem

Bones: p84–85

1. a) elbow

2. b) vitamin D

3. a) ankle

4. a) leg

5. a) calcium

6. a) around 206

More true or false?: p86–87

1. True; 2. False; 3. False;
4. True; 5. True; 6. False; 7.
False; 8. True; 9. True ; 10.
True

Living things: p88–89

1. a) cat
2. a) sheep
3. b) cow
4. a) clown
5. b) froglet
6. a) 14
7. a) fungus
8. c) butterfly

Missing letters: p90–91

1. current
2. temperature
3. poles
4. oxygen
5. lever
6. friction
7. hydrogen
8. virus

Body word search: p92

F	I	N	G	E	R	P	A
E	R	J	B	L	O	F	N
N	O	S	E	B	E	T	K
S	A	Q	I	O	X	G	L
L	G	D	N	W	T	W	E
K	E	E	H	C	Z	E	V
C	Y	M	A	J	H	Y	K
S	H	O	U	L	D	E	R

HISTORY

Ancient history: p94–95

1. b) iron
2. a) blue
3. c) Romans
4. a) Romulus and Remus
5. a) Roman
6. a) Egyptian

Myths and legends: p96–97

1. b) Hercules
2. b) heart
3. a) Anubis
4. a) snakes
5. c) Sphinx
6. b) Thor

Modern history: p98–99

1. b) Berlin
2. a) writer
3. c) rationing
4. c) Second World War
5. c) Second World War
6. a) Barack Obama
7. b) Tutankhamun
8. a) Russia

Travel and technology: p100–101

1. Victoria
2. Stephenson
3. 19th
4. 1912
5. Gutenberg
6. First World
7. 20th

Odd one out: p102–103

1. Hatshepsut – she was an Egyptian Pharaoh, the others were Roman emperors
2. Meiji – it is a Japanese period, the others are Chinese dynasties
3. Zeus – he's a Greek god, the rest are Norse gods
4. Gold Age – it is not an archaeological period
5. Acropolis – it was built by ancient Greeks, the others were built by ancient Romans
6. Great Ziggurat of Ur – it was in ancient Mesopotamia, the others are ancient Egyptian

Ancient Egypt: p104–105

1. a) The body of a lion and the head of a pharaoh
2. b) the Nile
3. b) Cleopatra
4. b) the Valley of the Kings
5. a) Nefertiti

Ancient Greece: p106–107

1. b) stone
2. c) three
3. b) Athena
4. b) Aristotle
5. a) Sparta
6. a) Acropolis

Ancient Rome: p108–109

1. c) Vesuvius
2. b) Londinium
3. c) V and M (V = 5; L = 50; C = 100; M = 1,000)
4. c) Virgil
5. c) The Colosseum

6. b) centurions

Brave new worlds: p110–111

1. a) Spain
2. a) James Cook
3. b) Ferdinand Magellan
4. c) Amelia Earhart
5. c) Neil Armstrong
6. a) Christopher Columbus
7. a) Nellie Bly

Famous dates: p112–113

1. b) Second World War
2. a) Independence Day
3. a) Bastille Day
4. a) First World War
5. a) American Revolution
6. a) 1889

Inventions: p114–115

1. a) 1903
2. b) Karl Benz
3. b) Alexander Graham Bell
4. a) Alexander Fleming
5. a) Ladislao and Georg Biro
7. a) Marie Curie

Modern history alphabet: p116–120

A Amy; B battles; C Christopher Columbus; D Dog; E England; F France; G George; H Henry VIII; I Ireland; J Jersey; K Kingdom; L lights; M Merkel; N November 11, 1918; O Operation Sealion; P Pearl Harbor; Q Queen Elizabeth II; R Roald; S Second World War; T Tank; U USSR; V Versailles; W Wilson; X Axis – yes, we know it's cheating as it doesn't begin with X!; Y Ypres; Z There is no Z! Can you think of a modern history question whose answer begins with Z?

GEOGRAPHY

Cities around the world: p122–123

1. b) Japan

2. c) Spain

3. b) London

4. a) Italy

5. b) Australia

6. a) France

Capital cities: True or false?: p124–125

1. False; 2. True; 3. False; 4. False; 5. False; 6. False; 7. True; 8. False; 9. True; 10. True

Flags: p126–127

1. red; 2. blue; 3. Mexico; 4. 3; 5. white; 6. 2; 7. white

Physical geography: p128–129

1. b) lava

2. a) longitude

3. c) Pacific

4. b) South America

5. b) river

6. a) Etna

USA: p130–131

1. b) Pacific Ocean

2. b) Canada

3. a) Atlantic Ocean

4. c) California

5. c) New

6. b) California

Countries: p132–133

1. a) Sweden

2. b) USA

3. b) Asia

4. b) Mexico

5. a) Germany

6. b) Canada

7. b) Spain

8. a) Australia

Countries: True or false?: p134–135

1. True; 2. False; 3. False; 4. True; 5. True; 6. False; 7. False; 8. False

Hidden monument:

p136–137

```
  T O K Y O
 T H A M E S
       J E R U S A L E M
H O C H I M I N H C I T Y
     P A R A G U A Y
       H I R O S H I M A
 N O R W A Y
     L I M A
```

UK: p138–139

1. a) Birmingham

2. c) Edinburgh

3. b) East Anglia

4. b) The Severn

5. b) Loch Morar

6. c) Wales

Confused capitals:

p140–141

1. Paris

2. Stockholm

3. Budapest

4. Copenhagen

5. Cairo

6. Moscow

Australia and New Zealand:

p142–143

1. c) Darwin

2. b) Uluru

3. a) Papua New Guinea

4. c) Tasman Sea

5. b) Lake Taupo

6. a) Southern Alps

Match the cities: p144–145

Japan: Osaka, Kyoto, Fukushima

Spain: Seville, Valencia, Barcelona

Italy: Naples, Venice, Florence

Australia: Melbourne, Canberra, Perth

Canada: Vancouver, Montreal, Ottawa

India: Mumbai, Kolkata, Delhi

More flags: p146–147

1. Norway, Iceland

2. Finland, Greece

3. Romania

4. Australia, New Zealand

Missing letters: p148–149

1. Richter

2. plates

3. reservoir

4. tributary

5. monsoon

6. cumulonimbus

7. longitude

8. Greenland

9. avalanche

10. Australia

Missing places: p150–151

1. South America

2. Sweden

3. Spain

4. Africa

5. Spain

6. Peru

7. Brazil

Starting with 'S': p152-153

1. Switzerland; 2. South; 3. Scandinavia ; 4. Sydney ; 5. Seine ; 6. South America; 7. San Marino ; 8. Sardinia

True or false?: p154–155

1. False; 2. True; 3. True; 4. False ; 5. False; 6. False; 7. True; 8. False

Mix-up:

p156–157

1. Beijing

2. Pyrenees

3. Pacific

4. meander

5. Canberra

6. Ecuador, Colombia, Venezuela, Brazil, Bolivia, Peru

7. delta

European countries: p158

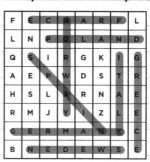

Mountains crossword: p159

Weather word search: p160

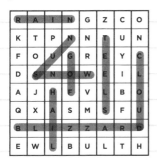

TEST THE TEACHER

Books: p162–163

1. b) Hogsmeade
2. a) Toothless
3. a) Snozzcumber
4. b) Albus Dumbledore
5. c) League
6. c) *Billionaire Girl*

Film: p164–165

1. b) *Cars*
2. b) Kylo Ren
3. a) *Pirates of the Caribbean*
4. c) *Despicable Me*
5. c) Japan
6. b) Tony Stark
7. a) Optimus Prime
8. c) Sven

Music: p166–167

1. b) Katy Perry
2. b) Beyoncé
3. a) Louis Tomlinson
4. c) Australia
5. b) Coldplay
6. a) Lorde
7. b) 1989

Gaming: p168–169

1. c) purple
2. b) Yoshi
3. a) Eevee
4. b) Jigglypuff
5. b) experience points
6. b) *Fortnite*

Tech: p170–171

1. a) Sony
2. b) Microsoft
3. a) memory
4. c) light
5. c) tablet
6. b) mouse
7. c) A
8. a) System

Sport: p172–173

1. b) Serbian
2. a) manual
3. b) Barcelona
4. c) Milan
5. b) Ollie
6. a) Portuguese
7. c) Lewis Hamilton

Fashion: p174–175

1. c) sunglasses
2. a) jumpsuit
3. c) necklace
4. b) Kanye West
5. a) Ivy Park
6. c) New York

Acronyms: p176–177

1. b) head
2. a) feel when
3. c) I don't get it
4. b) laugh out loud
5. a) I know right
6. b) be right back
7. b) for the win
8. a) too much information

TV: p178

1. a) pineapple
2. a) Gunther
3. b) Ned Flanders
4. a) *Adventure Time*